Sloan the Sloth's Positive Affirmations

Workbook and Activities

For Boys and Girls, Ages 7-11

PUNK AND FRIENDS

by Misty Black

Berry Patch Press

www.berrypatchpress.com

Positive-Affirmations Workbook for Boys and Girls, ages 7-11
Companion workbook to *Sloan the Sloth Loves Being Different:*
A Self-Worth Story
Punk and Friends Learn Social Skills Series

Based on the book written by Misty Black
Hand-drawn illustrations by Marina Batrak and Ana Rankovic
Graphic design by Misty Black Media, LLC

For copyright permission, school visits, and
book readings/signings, email
mistyblackauthor@gmail.com.

Paperback ISBN: 978-1-951292-32-4

First Edition 2020

Berry Patch Press LLC
www.berrypatchpress.com

This is the companion
Positive-Affirmations Workbook and Activities
to *Sloan the Sloth Loves Being Different:
A Self-Worth Story*

To sign up for new releases, promotions, and to get a free
eBook visit www.berrypatchpress.com.

For fundraising opportunities, email
mistyblackauthor@gmail.com.

I love hearing from my readers.

Follow on Social Media
✉ mistyblackauthor@gmail.com
⬤ Misty Black Author ⬤ Misty Black Author

The best way to support an author is to provide a review
on Amazon and/or Goodreads.

Thank you!

Misty Black

Draw or place a picture of yourself in the frame below.

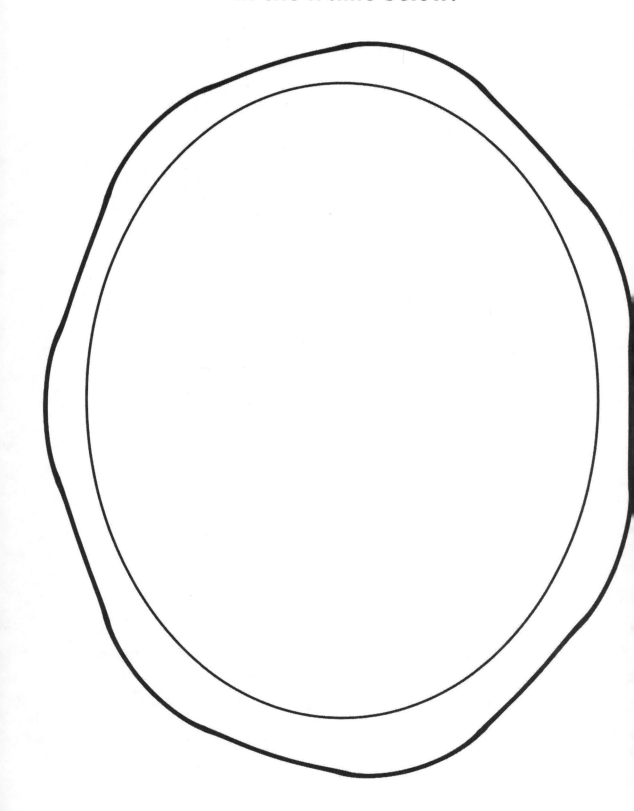

ALL ABOUT ME

Fill in the blanks to write a little bit about yourself.

My name is...   I am   years old.
_____

My favorite subject in school is...
_____

My favorite things to do are...
_____
_____

My best friend is...
_____

I am happiest when...
_____
_____

The people in my family are...
_____
_____

My family is important to me because...
_____
_____

When I grow up, I want to be...
_____

I am most proud of...
_____
_____

I am important, and what I think matters.

I AM LOVED

Make a list of the people who love you and what they love about you.

It feels good to love and be loved.

Draw a picture of you with someone you love.

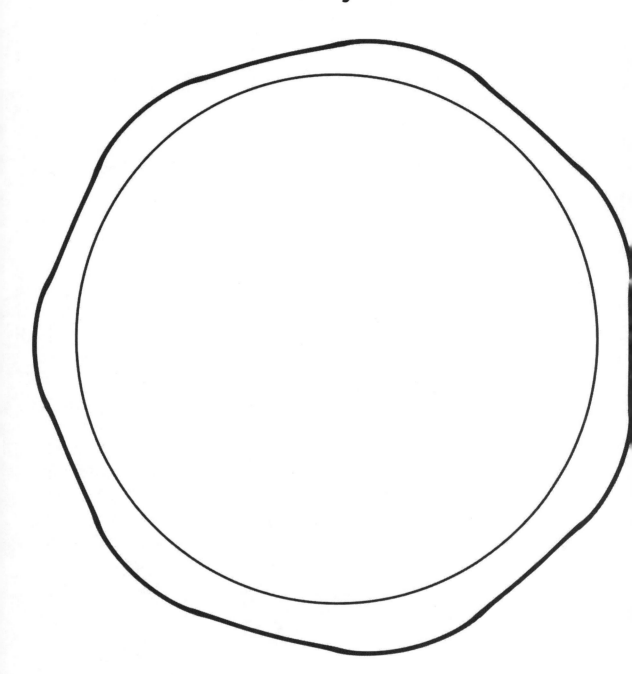

How do you feel when you're with this person?

HELP GRUNT THE GRIZZLY FIND MONKEY SO HE CAN GIVE HER A FLOWER.

start

I AM BRAVE

You can do things that are hard. Make a list of things you've done that seemed scary to you.

Failure is a stepping stone to success.

I AM SMART

You are always learning. What things do you know now that you didn't know when you were younger?

_____

_____

_____

_____

_____

_____

_____

_____

_____

_____

_____

_____

_____

Learning helps my mind to grow.

I AM GRATEFUL

Make a list of things you're thankful for. Draw a picture of a few of those things on the next page.

When I'm grateful, I can see all the good surrounding me.

Being grateful helps me to be happy.

I AM KIND

Make a list of things you've done that have made other people happy.

Service is a gift from the heart.

I HAVE GOALS AND DREAMS

Write down some goals and dreams you have for the future and how it will make you feel to achieve those goals?

_____

_____

_____

_____

_____

_____

_____

_____

_____

_____

_____

_____

_____

Goals help keep me focused.

Draw some pictures of yourself achieving
your goals in the future. Post these pictures around your
room to remind you of the things you're working towards.

I AM HONEST

Integrity means that you're honest even when no one is watching. What have you done to show you have integrity?

I strive to be truthful to myself and others.

I AM CONFIDENT

Confidence means you believe in yourself. What have you done because you believed you could?

I am happy when I do my best. My best is good enough.

HELP SKIT THE SQUIRREL TO STOP LOOKING IN THE MIRROR AND FIND THE HEART

I LOVE MY LIFE

Make a list of things you love about your life.

I have the ability to make my life great.

I AM HAPPY

Make a list of things you do that make you happy.

I choose to be happy by doing things
that bring me joy every day.

**Draw some pictures of you doing things
that make you happy.**

I FOCUS ON THE GOOD

Make a list of things that are good about your life.

Even when hard things are happening around me,
I can find good things if I look for them.

FIND THE HIDDEN WORDS, THEN USE THEM AS "I AM" STATEMENTS

Z	R	K	A	M	W	S	T	E	Y	S	O	D	P	E	N	S	D
H	C	R	C	W	T	H	A	K	Y	M	G	P	F	I	G	O	Y
A	A	N	S	F	K	E	L	X	U	T	W	H	U	Q	Y	P	H
S	R	U	R	H	C	H	E	S	X	U	H	K	N	E	S	T	S
K	I	A	S	D	A	R	N	X	G	U	Q	X	F	A	H	L	U
R	N	Y	V	W	A	I	T	K	S	N	T	L	D	E	A	P	D
H	G	F	S	Y	D	L	E	O	R	Q	P	Z	P	L	M	O	J
S	Q	I	L	O	V	E	D	M	S	F	E	G	Q	O	T	F	P
P	F	B	V	A	P	G	M	T	G	I	V	I	N	G	S	K	T
D	R	E	D	I	J	S	N	A	R	H	R	A	D	J	X	O	B
W	N	S	B	O	T	A	L	H	A	P	P	Y	W	Z	H	R	R
P	S	M	A	R	T	N	P	E	T	D	W	D	Y	E	F	R	A
F	Q	G	R	R	E	V	M	S	E	S	D	S	J	A	P	X	V
D	M	P	O	Y	H	D	T	P	F	T	L	W	Y	Y	A	S	E
Y	E	P	R	V	D	P	Y	F	U	N	M	H	E	Z	P	I	Y
F	M	Y	B	J	O	Y	F	U	L	S	G	P	D	X	F	S	J
I	E	S	N	M	Q	A	I	N	D	F	O	A	T	L	K	M	E

HAPPY	BRAVE
JOYFUL	SMART
GRATEFUL	FUN
LOVED	CARING
TALENTED	GIVING
HONEST	IMPORTANT

I AM IMPORTANT

The things you do matter. Make a list of your abilities and talents.

I am one of a kind.
My talents are unique and make me special.

Draw a picture of yourself doing one of your talents.

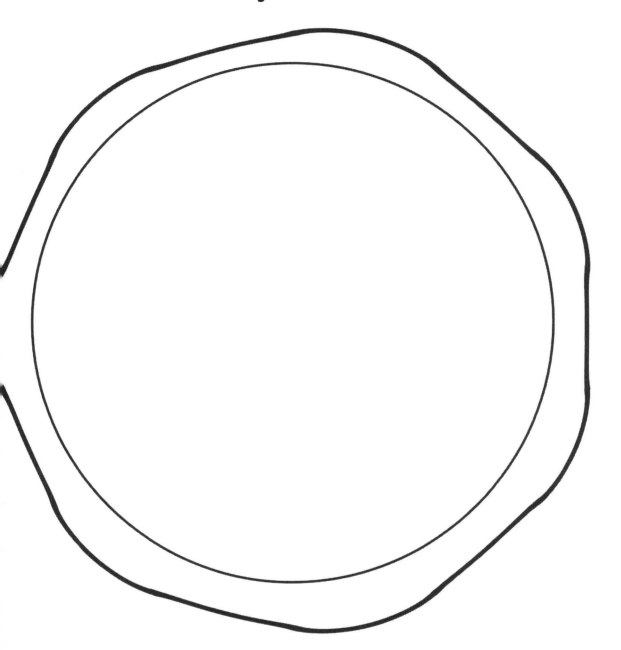

How does it make you feel when you're good at something?

DRAWING IS A TALENT. LEARN TO DRAW AN EAGLE.

Use the bottom grid to copy and draw the eagle pictured in the top grid. It might help to focus on copying one square at a time.

COLOR BY NUMBER

①RED   ④GREEN
②ORANGE ⑤BLUE
③YELLOW ⑥PURPLE

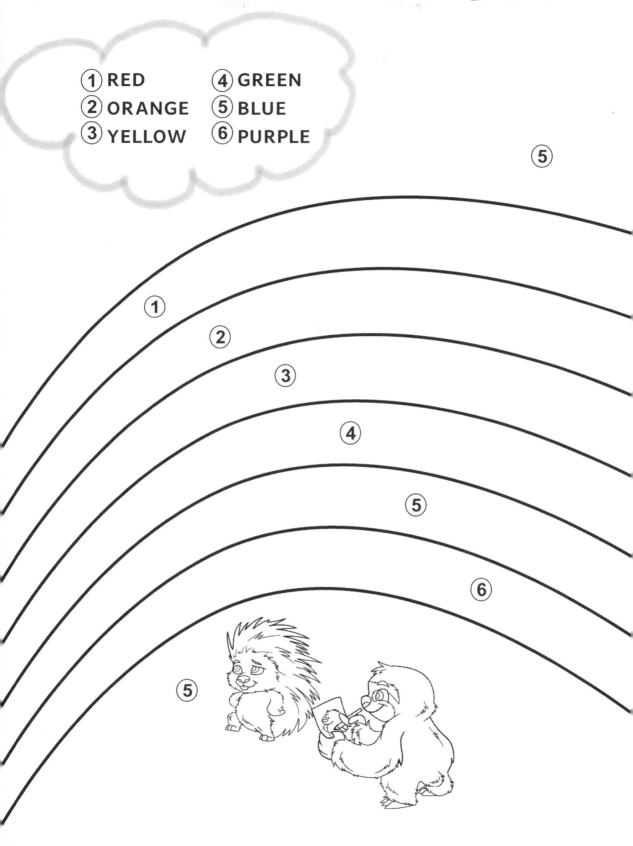

I HELP MAKE THE WORLD A BETTER PLACE
How do you improve the world around you?

You are meant to be great.

I TAKE CARE OF MYSELF

What do you do to take care of your body and mind?

I strive to keep my mind and body
clean so I can always feel my best.

Draw some pictures of what you do to take care of yourself.

Color and cut out the affirmations on the next page. Place them on your mirror or in a place where you can see them often. Read them out loud whenever you see them.

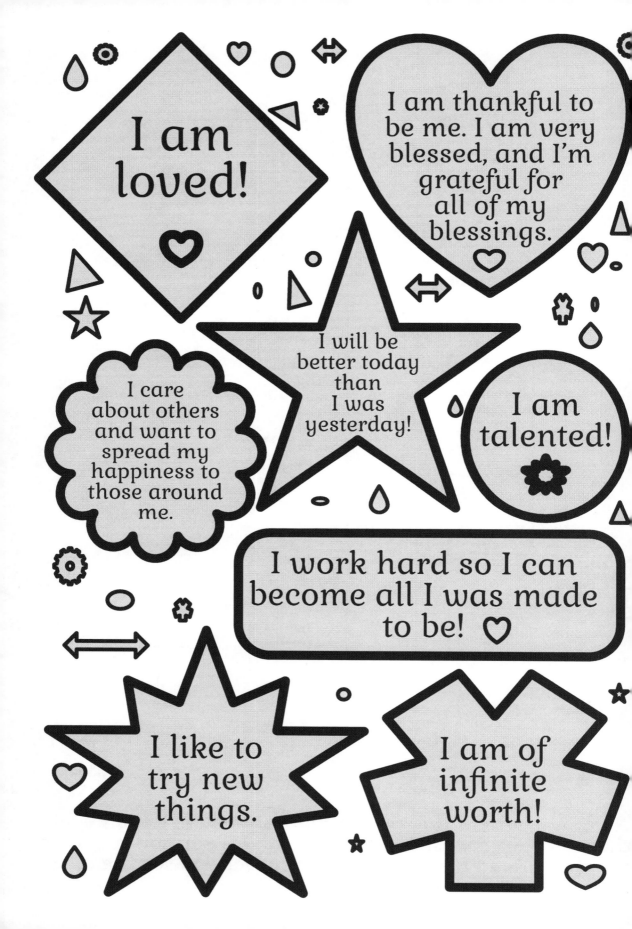

THE DOT GAME

Objective:
Connect the dots to form a square. The player who forms the most squares wins.

How to Play:
Player 1 starts by drawing a horizontal or vertical line between any two adjacent dots.
Then Player 2 also makes a horizontal or vertical line between any two adjacent dots.
Player 1 goes again and play continues back and forth.
When a player draws a line that forms a square, that player fills in the square with their color or with their first initial. The player who drew the closing line on the square gets another turn.
Continue until all the squares have been filled in, then count up your squares.

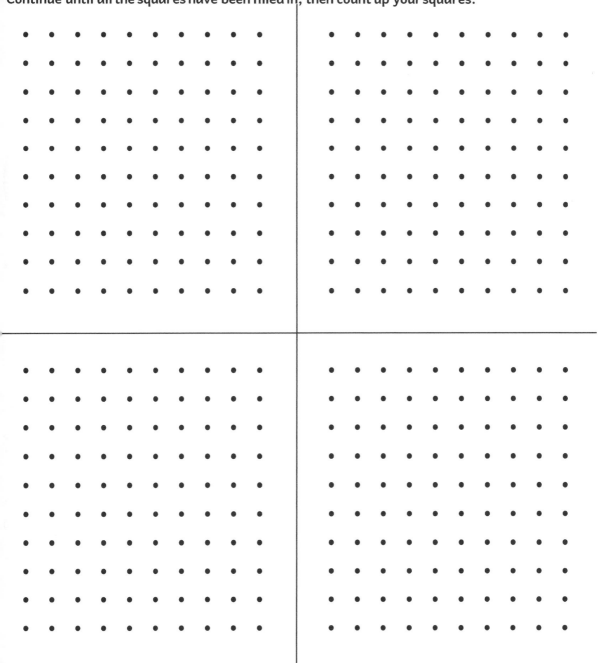

I HAVE GOOD DAYS

Write a story about one of your favorite days.
What did you like most about it?

_____

_____

_____

_____

_____

_____

_____

_____

_____

_____

_____

_____

When I am happy, I am able to share
my happiness with others.

I CAN OVERCOME

Write about a time you were struggling and how you overcame the struggle.

_____

_____

_____

_____

_____

_____

_____

_____

_____

_____

_____

I watch for the rainbows after the rain.

I IMPROVE MYSELF EVERYDAY

What are some things you're working on to become better?

I strive to be better today than I was yesterday.

I AM A GOOD FRIEND

Make a list of your friends. Write what you do to show your friends you care about them.

I have good friends because I am a good friend.

TIC-TAC-TOE

Play Tic-Tac-Toe with a friend.

What do you like to do with your friends?

Draw or place some pictures of you with your friends.

Write your own positive affirmations in the shapes on the next couple of pages. Color and cut them out as well. Use them as a daily reminder that you are amazing and you can handle hard things.

VISION BOARD

A vision board is a way for you to see your goals and dreams on a daily basis.

Ask your parents for help if you need it. Get a poster board and cut out images and words from a magazine that represent your goals for this week, month, or year. Get permission before using scissors, glue, or cutting up any magazines. Glue or tape your clippings onto the poster board. Write around the clippings on the poster to remind you of the things they represent if needed. You can also use some of the positive affirmation shapes from the previous pages on your vision board.

Place the vision board somewhere where you can see it everyday to remind you of the things you're working towards. Being visually reminded of your goals and dreams is very powerful. Look at the vision board every day and imagine how you will feel when you accomplish your goals.

Write in the space below some of the things you want to include on your vision board.

I LOVE MYSELF

What are some things you love about yourself?

Loving myself isn't selfish.
When I love myself, I am better at loving others.

Draw or place a picture of yourself in the mirror below. Write several compliments about yourself around the picture. Then look in a real mirror and say those things out loud to yourself. Sometimes, you have to hear and see yourself saying them out loud in order to really believe them.

LEARN TO DRAW SNAKE

Use the bottom grid to copy and draw the image pictured in the top grid. It might help to focus on copying one square at a time.

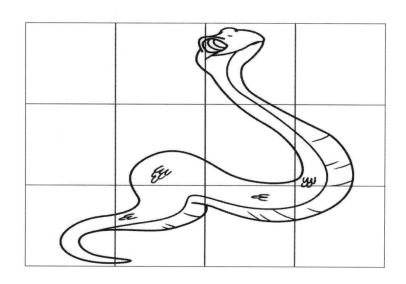

NEGATIVE THOUGHTS

Write down all the negative thoughts you have about yourself. Get them all out.

These thoughts will be used in an activity on the next page, then you will rip up this page along with all the negative thoughts and get rid of them.

This page is meant to be torn out here.

_____

_____

_____

_____

_____

_____

_____

_____

_____

_____

_____

This page is meant to be torn out here

After you're done writing the negative thoughts, write the opposite of those negative thoughts on the next page. Turn each negative thought into a positive one. Use those positive thoughts as affirmations by repeating the new positive thoughts as "I am" statements 3 times a day.

Now, take this page and tear it out of the book. Rip it into tiny pieces and throw those pieces away. Get rid of those destructive thoughts and replace them with positive things.

POSITIVE THOUGHTS

Now take the negative thoughts from the previous page and turn them into positive thoughts.

Knowing how to change my negative thoughts and emotions into positive ones gives me the power to be happy.

Writing a journal is a great way to remember the good things in your life and reduce stress. Use the following journal pages to record any thoughts, feelings, or events you'd like to remember or understand more clearly.

You could also use the following pages to write a kind note to a friend or loved one. Mail it to them, stick it under their door, put it in their lunch box or back pack, or give it to them with a treat.

There are so many ways to show someone that you care.

Other books by Misty Black:

<u>With Love Book Series:</u>

You Taught Me Love: Picture book and companion coloring/activity book

When You Feel Better: Picture book and companion coloring/activity books

Grandmas Are for Love: Picture book, companion coloring book,

and companion *Grandma's Stories Guided Journal.*

<u>Punk and Friends Series:</u>

Punk the Skunk Learns to Say Sorry

Can Quilliam Learn to Control His Temper

Brave the Beaver Has the Worry Warts

Sloan the Sloth Loves Being Different: A Self-Worth Story

Positive Affirmations Workbook and Activities

Grunt the Grizzly Learns to Be Grateful

Grunt the Grizzly's Gratitude Journal

<u>Fizzle Fun Series:</u>

Unicorns, Magic, and Slime, Oh My!

My Mom the Fairy

Do you own a store or need a fundraiser?

Wholesale discounts on hardcover bulk order purchases are available on select books. Email mistyblackauthor@gmail.com for details.

Please consider leaving a review.
It would be greatly appreciated.

Made in the USA
Columbia, SC
19 December 2022

74598149R00048